ISBN 979-8-9854985-0-9 (Paperback)

First Edition

www.natasaz.com

"Mommy, Who is This Lady?"

(A Love Letter from Your "Kind Of" Aunt)

Written by Natasa Zoubouridis

Illustrated by Katie Williams

Dedicated to: Antonia, Evelyn & Anesti

Special thanks to Anna, Marina, and their husbands
for making these kids and letting me be their "kind of" aunt.

Thanks to my editors Jeph, Emily, Amanda, and everyone that gave me feedback.

And to the greatest Zia this world has known, thank you to Elena Zanfei for always being there,
inspiring me, wiping my tears when I felt lost, and building me up when I felt broken.

There is no better "Kind Of" Aunt than you.

As you get older you might ask yourself,
"How are we related?"

You call me "Aunt,"
but I'm not really your aunt.

1

You see, I'm your mommy's best friend.

Probably her only friend until you came along,
but we won't get into that.

I met your mommy when she was a young girl heading to school to become a grown woman.

Together we had many adventures,
made many mistakes,
and created a lot of memories.

We helped shape each other into the women we are today through long late-night talks over late-night tacos after late-night...

I was there for new schools, new jobs, new friends,

...and new fashion statements.

I was there when she discovered her confidence,

and I was there as she fell in love with your daddy.

I was there when she got married,

moved into her first house,

...and most importantly, I was there when she had you.

Sweetheart, you will come to learn relatives are
given to you, but family is chosen.

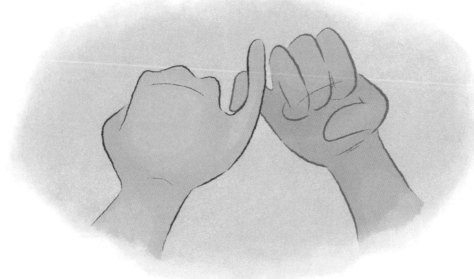

Your mommy and I chose to love each other
just how I have chosen to love you.

So, I'm not your aunt
by law or family,
but I love you.

I will protect you and be someone you can trust.

I will change your diapers
and teach you about self-love,

classic movies, good music,
and the best stand-up comedy.

I will always be there to kiss your boo-boos,

listen to your heartbreak,

pick you up from a
late-night party,

and even help you with
your homework if you need.

No, my sweetheart, we may not share a last name,
but we are family.

And I love you just the same.

About the Author
Natasa Zoubouridis

Natasa Zoubouridis has spent 10 years in the comedy and production industry as a writer, entrepreneur, and TV producer. She spent the beginning of her career collecting jokes and making videos for kids with cancer. She then went on to produce the first late-night comedy show in Chicago, WGN-TV's "Man of the People with Pat Tomasulo".

She is currently running the youtube channel: Everything House, and embodying the "Fun Aunt" lifestyle everyday.

Having gotten a bachelor's in creative writing she finally wrote her first book "Mommy, Who is This Lady?" with the help of her muses; her "kind of" nieces and nephew.

Made in the USA
Las Vegas, NV
17 February 2024

85890292R00017